The Nineties

23 classic songs for keyboard

© International Music Publications Ltd
First published in 1995 by International Music Publications Ltd
International Music Publications Ltd is a Faber Music company
3 Queen Square, London WC1N 3AU
Music arranged and processed by Barnes Music Engraving Ltd
Cover image Alamy Images
Printed in England by Caligraving Ltd
All rights reserved

ISBN 0-571-52567-9

CRAZY FOR YOU

Words and Music by Richard Wermerling

Suggested Registration: Piano
Rhythm: 16 Beat
Tempo: ♩ = 102

In - tu - i - tion tells me what I'm miss - ing when I

look at____ you,____ so tell me hon - ey, am I

dream-ing, or____ do you feel it____ too?____

'Cause I feel that you__ know, ah, you've got me

just where you want__ me.__ I'm cra - zy, cra - zy for

you,_____ and there's no-thing that I won't do. I'm caught by the

CROCODILE SHOES

Words and Music by Tony McAnaney

Suggested Registration: Harmonica
Rhythm: Country
Tempo: ♩ = 124

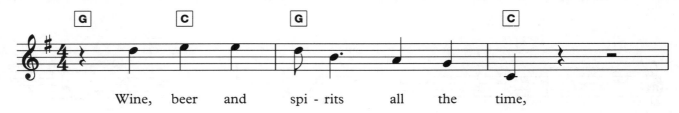

Wine, beer and spi - rits all the time,

though I____ have you,____ still she's al - ways on____ my

mind. The rain____ falls down,

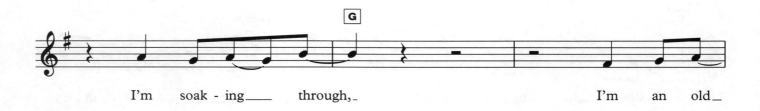

I'm soak - ing____ through,__ I'm an old__

__ man in - side a young__ man's shoes.

My cro - co - dile shoes are__ cry - ing too,

for they know how much love I have__ for you.__

Cro - co - dile shoes,_____ cro - co - dile shoes,

cro - co - dile shoes,_____ cro - co - dile

shoes,_____ cro - co - dile shoes,_____

cro - co - dile shoes, cro - co - dile shoes,_____

cro - co - dile shoes._____

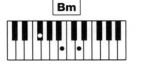 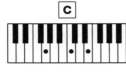 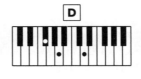 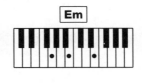 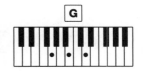

HOLD ME, THRILL ME, KISS ME

Words and Music by Harry Noble

Suggested Registration: Electric Piano
Rhythm: Slow Rock 6/8
Tempo: ♩ = 72

Hold me,__ hold me,__ ne-ver let me go un-til you've told me,__ told me,__

what I want to know, and then just hold me,__ hold me,__ make me tell you I'm in love with

you. Thrill me,__ thrill me,__ walk me down the lane where sha-dows

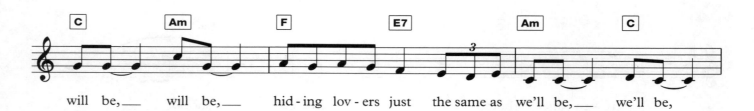

will be,__ will be,__ hid-ing lov-ers just the same as we'll be,__ we'll be,

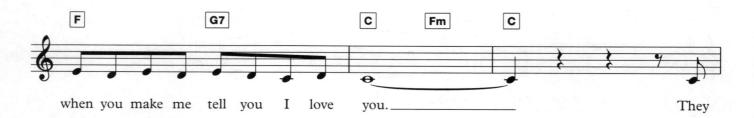

when you make me tell you I love you._____ They

told me, 'Be sen-si-ble___ with your new love,__ don't be

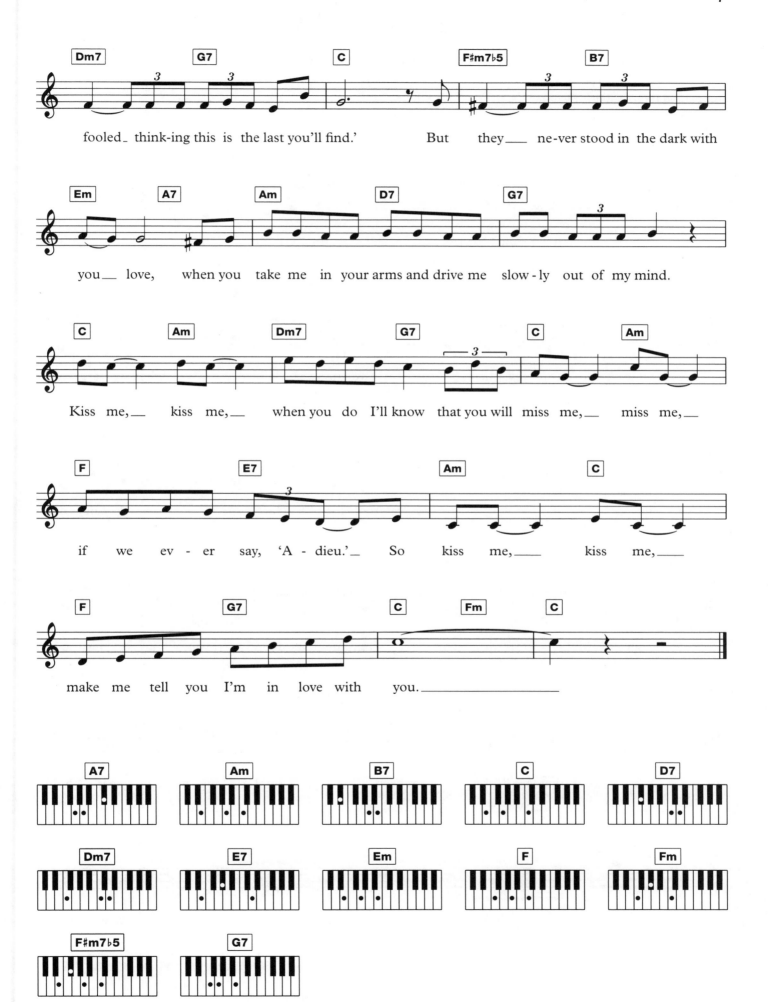

Holding On

Words and Music by Beverley Craven

Suggested Registration: Piano
Rhythm: Soft Rock
Tempo: ♩ = 90

I'm los-ing con-trol____ of my e-mo-tions, you've ____ got this hold on my heart____ I've ne-ver known, what we are feel- ing,____ you____ ne-ver took me so far.____ I can't find ____ the words. Is this love?____ Tell me I've found____ you. Is this love? _____ Say that you'll al-ways keep hold-ing on, keep hold- -ing on,_____ 'cause your love's____ got a hold on____ me.____ Keep hold-

I Drove All Night

Words and Music by Billy Steinberg and Tom Kelly

Suggested Registration: Distorted Guitar
Rhythm: Rock
Tempo: ♩ = 124

I had to es - cape,___ the ci - ty was stic - ky and cruel,_____

___ may - be I should have called__ you first,__ but I was

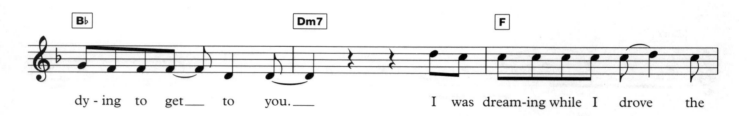

dy - ing to get__ to you.__ I was dream-ing while I drove the

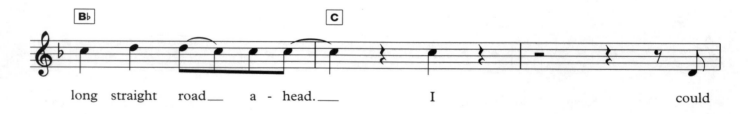

long straight road__ a - head.__ I could

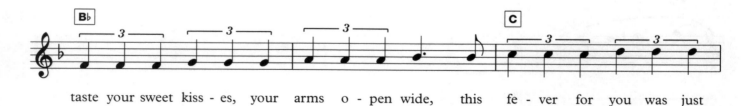

taste your sweet kiss - es, your arms o - pen wide, this fe - ver for you was just

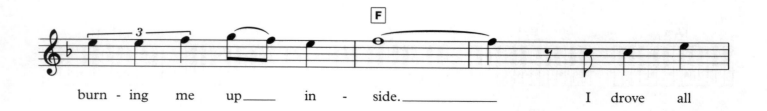

burn - ing me up___ in - side._____ I drove all

night_____ to get to you,

is that all right? I drove all

night,_____ crept in your room,

woke you from your sleep to make love___ to

you, is that all right?__

I drove all night._____

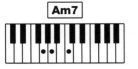
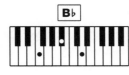
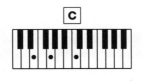
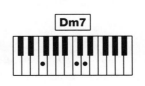
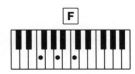

I Swear

Words and Music by Frank Myers and Gary Baker

Suggested Registration: Electric Piano
Rhythm: Soft Rock
Tempo: ♩ = 88

I see the ques - tions in your eyes,_

_ I know what's weigh - ing on _ your mind,_ but you can be sure

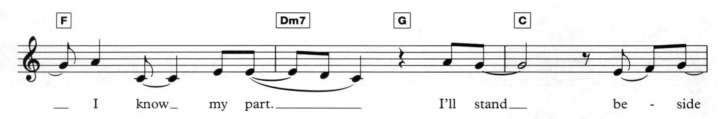

_ I know_ my part._ I'll stand_ be - side

_ you through the years,_ you'll on - ly cry_ those hap - py tears,

_ and though I'll make_ mis - takes, I'll ne - ver break_ your heart.

_ I swear_ by the moon_ and the stars_ in the sky,

I'll Make Love To You

Words and Music by Kenny Edmonds

Suggested Registration: Saxophone
Rhythm: Slow Rock 6/8
Tempo: ♩. = 56

JUST ANOTHER DAY

Words and Music by Jon Secada and Miguel A Morejon

Suggested Registration: Jazz Organ
Rhythm: 16 Beat
Tempo: ♩ = 116

Morn-ings a - lone, _____ when you come home ___ I breathe

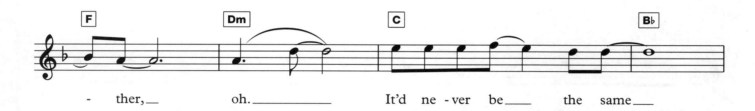

___ a lit - tle fast - er, _____ ev - ery time we're ___ to - ge -

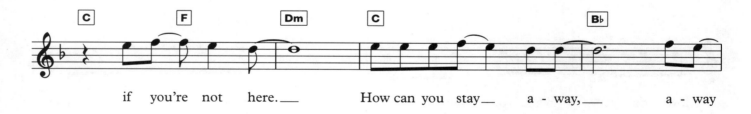

- ther, ___ oh. _____ It'd ne -ver be ___ the same ___

if you're not here. ___ How can you stay ___ a - way, ___ a - way

___ so long? ___

Why can't we stay ___ to - ge - ther?

A Million Love Songs

Words and Music by Gary Barlow

Suggested Registration: Saxophone
Rhythm: Slow Rock 6/8
Tempo: ♩. = 72

Put your head a-gainst my life, what do you hear?

— A mil - lion words just try - ing to make the

love song of the year. Close your eyes, but

don't for - get____ what you have heard,____ a

man who's trying to say three words, words that make me

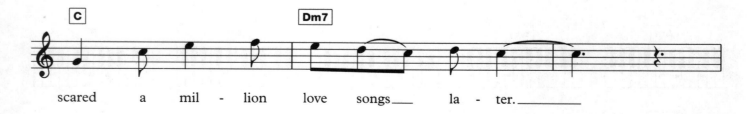

scared a mil - lion love songs____ la - ter._____

Here I_____ am try - ing to tell you_____ that I care a mil - lion love songs____ la - ter,_____ and here_____ I_____ am, here____ I am a mil - lion love songs_ la - ter,_____ here_____ I_____ am._____

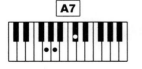 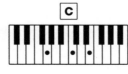 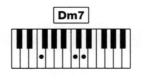 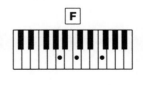 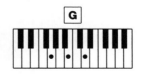

The One And Only

Words and Music by Nik Kershaw

Suggested Registration: Electric Guitar
Rhythm: Rock
Tempo: ♩ = 126

Call me,___ call me by___ my name, or___

call me by___ my num - ber.___ You put me through it,

I'll still be do - ing it my way. I do it, and yet___ you

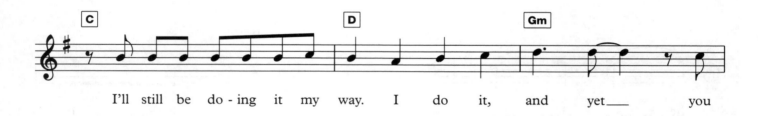

try to make___ me for - get___ who I real - ly

am. Don't tell me, I___ know best. I'm not the same

_ as all___ the rest.___ I am___ the one and on - ly,___

One Man In My Heart

Words and Music by Philip Oakey and Neil John Sutton

Suggested Registration: Vibraphone
Rhythm: 8 Beat
Tempo: ♩ = 97

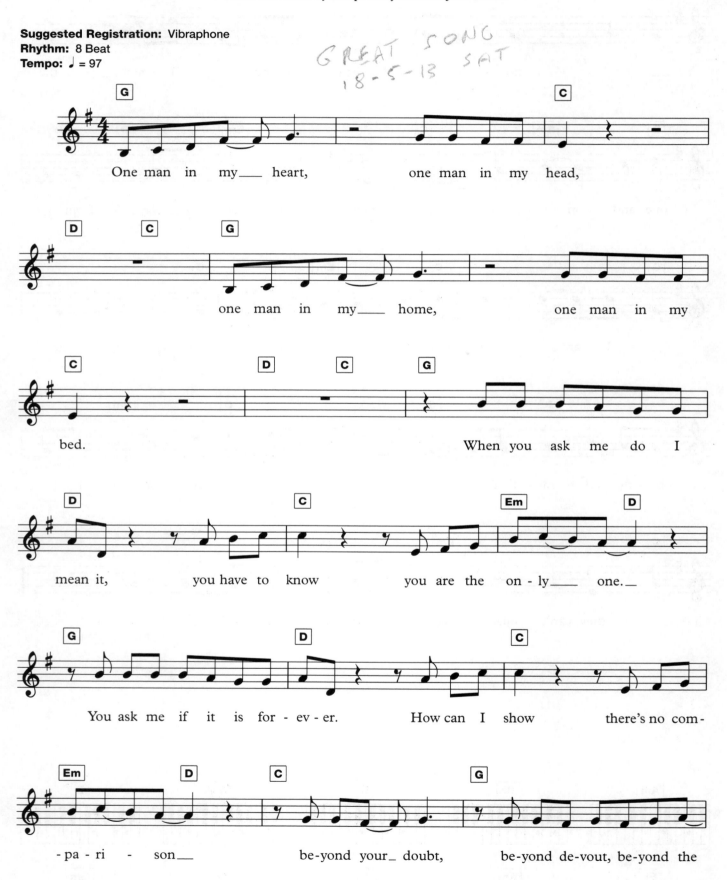

_stars____ to - night? One man in my___ heart,

one man in my head,

one man in my___ home, one man in my bed.

One man in my___ heart, one man in my

head, one man in my___ home, one man in my

bed.

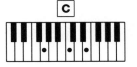 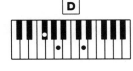 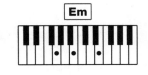 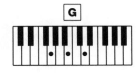

One Night Stand

Words and Music by Richard Wermerling

Suggested Registration: Saxophone
Rhythm: 8 Beat
Tempo: ♩ = 96

Give me your heart___ and I will make you a prom - ise,

give me your soul___ and I will be by your side for -

- ev - er girl, ___ and for - ev - er girl. ___

Give me your time___ and I will sav - our each mo - ment,

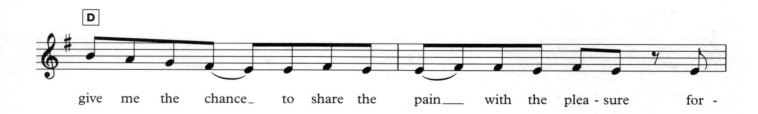

give me the chance_ to share the pain___ with the plea - sure for -

- ev - er girl, ___ and for - ev - er girl. ___

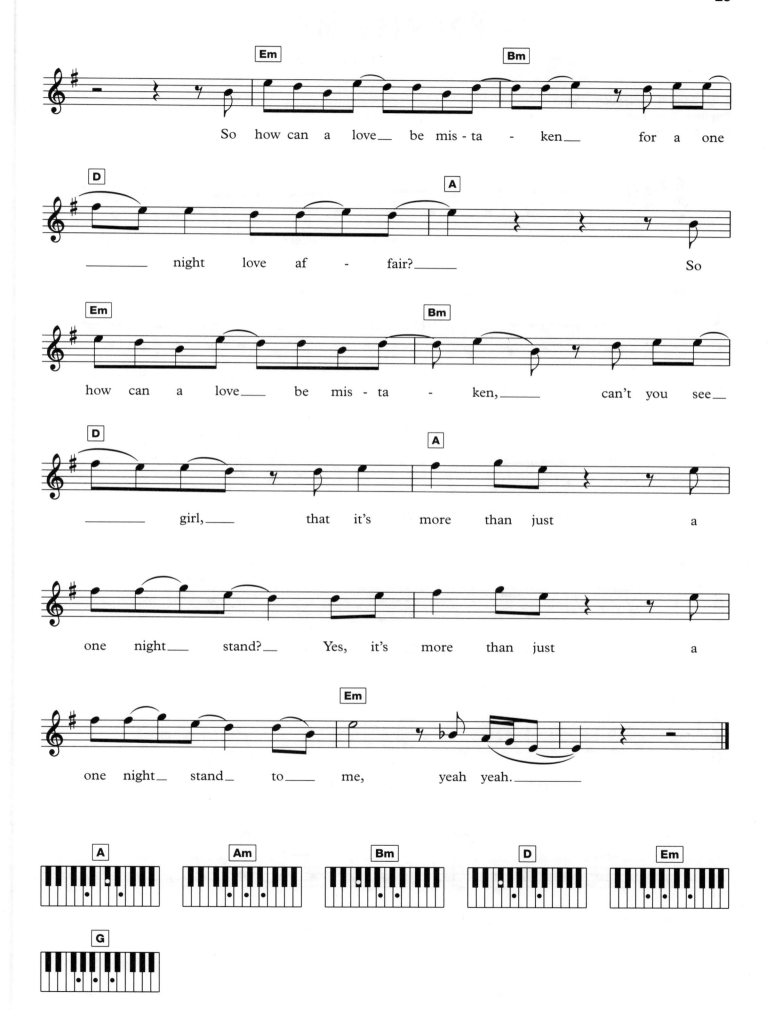

Promise Me

Words and Music by Beverley Craven

Suggested Registration: Piano
Rhythm: Soft Rock
Tempo: ♩ = 98

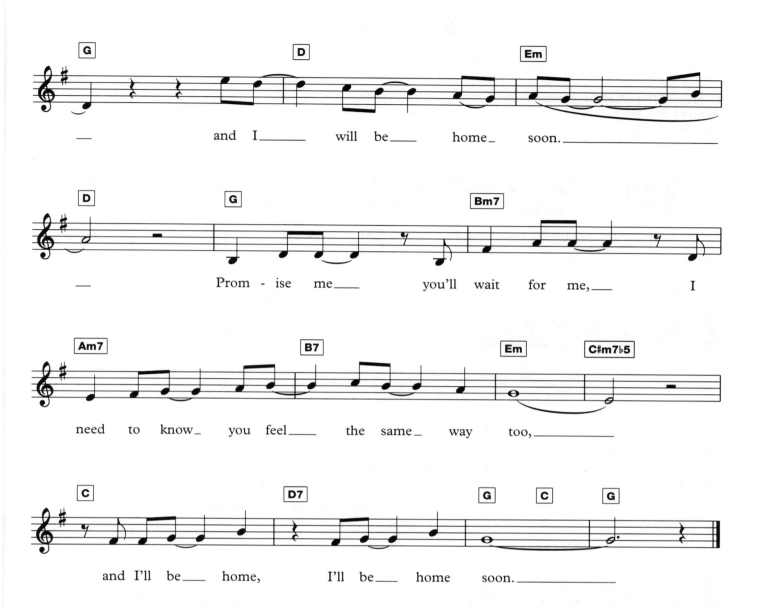

G   D   Em

— and I____ will be____ home_ soon._____

D   G   Bm7

— Prom - ise me____ you'll wait for me,____ I

Am7   B7   Em   C#m7♭5

need to know_ you feel____ the same_ way too,_____

C   D7   G   C   G

and I'll be____ home, I'll be____ home soon._____

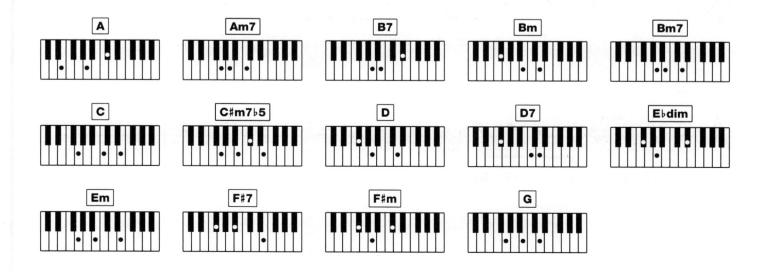

SACRIFICE

Words by Bernie Taupin / Music by Elton John

Suggested Registration: Electric Piano
Rhythm: Soft Rock
Tempo: ♩ = 116

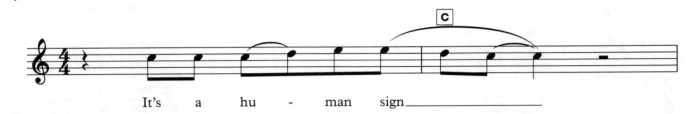

It's a hu - man sign _____

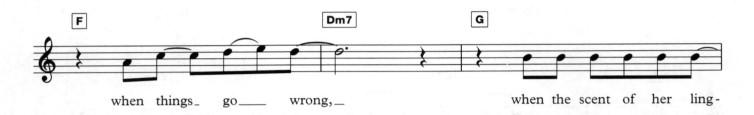

when things_ go_ wrong,_ when the scent of her ling-

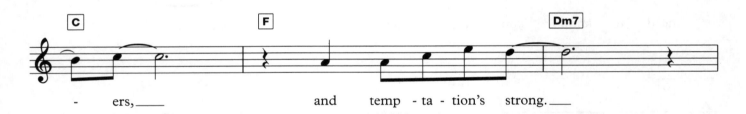

- ers,___ and temp - ta - tion's strong.___

In - to the boun - da - ry of each_ mar - ried mind,

_ sweet de - ceit comes a - call - in'___

and ne - ga - ti - vi - ty lands._ Cold, cold heart,_

Saltwater

Words and Music by Julian Lennon, Leslie Spiro and Mark Spiro

Suggested Registration: Acoustic Guitar
Rhythm: Soft Rock
Tempo: ♩ = 78

We are a rock re-volv-ing   a-round a gol-den sun,   we are a bil-lion child-ren

rolled in - to   one, __   so when I hear a-bout the   hole in the sky, __

salt - wa - ter wells in   my   eyes. __   We climb the high-est moun-tain,

we'll make the des-ert bloom,   we're so in - ge-nious we can   walk on the   moon,

but when I hear of how the   for-ests have died,   salt-wa-ter wells in   my   eyes.

__   I have lived for love,   but now that's not e-nough, for the

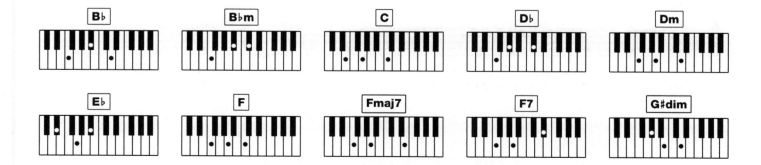

Sleeping Satellite

Words and Music by Tasmin Archer, John Beck and John Hughes

Suggested Registration: Flute
Rhythm: 16 Beat
Tempo: ♩ = 92

I blame you for the moon-lit sky,_____ and the dream that died_____ with the ea-gle's flight. I blame you for the

moon-lit nights when I won-der why_____ are the seas so dry?_____

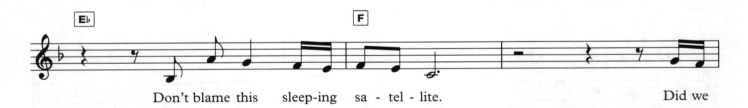

Don't blame this sleep-ing sa-tel-lite. Did we

fly to the moon too soon? Did we squan-der the chance in the rush of the

race? The rea-son we chase is lost in ro-mance,_____

and still we try_____ to jus-ti-fy the waste for a taste of man's

great - est ad - ven - ture oh.____ I blame you for the

moon - lit sky,____ and the dream that died____ with the

ea - gle's flight._ I blame you for the moon-lit nights when I

won-der why__ are the seas so dry?__ Don't blame this sleep-ing

sa - tel - lite._____

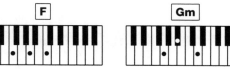

Someday (I'm Coming Back)

Words and Music by Stansfield, Devaney and Morris

Suggested Registration: Oboe
Rhythm: 8 Beat
Tempo: ♩ = 112

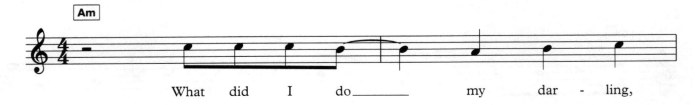

What did I do_____ my dar-ling,

that made you send___ me run-ning, told you to cast

__ me down, and throw_ me___ out?

What can I tell___ you hon-ey, if I___ don't_

know_ what I've done? All I can hope_ is that

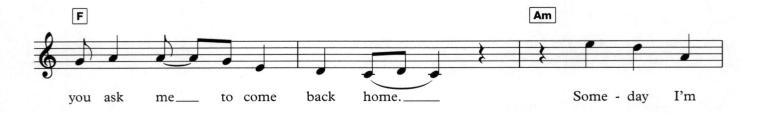

you ask me__ to come back home.___ Some-day I'm

com - ing back,_ and it won't_ be long be - fore you

call me,___ and tell me to___ come home.

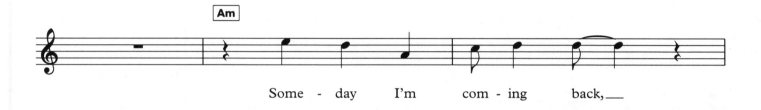

Some - day I'm com - ing back,___

and it won't_ be long be - fore I'm home,

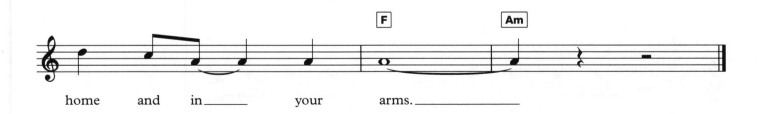

home and in___ your arms.___

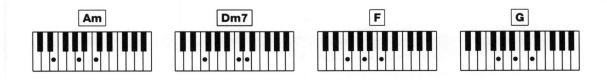

THESE ARE THE DAYS OF OUR LIVES

Words and Music by Queen

Suggested Registration: Marimba
Rhythm: Ethnic Rock / 8 Beat
Tempo: ♩ = 108

Some-times I get to feel-in' I was back in the old

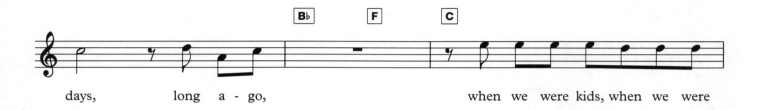

days, long a - go, when we were kids, when we were

young. Things seemed so per - fect, you know?

The days were end - less, we were cra - zy, we were young,

the sun was al - ways shin - in', we just lived for fun.___

Some-times, it seems like late - ly, I just don't know,

THINK TWICE

Words and Music by Pete Sinfield and Andy Hill

Suggested Registration: Flute
Rhythm: Soft Rock
Tempo: ♩ = 76

Don't think I can't feel that there's some - thing wrong, _

you've been the sweet-est part of my life for so _ long. I look in your eyes, there's a

dis - tant light, _ and you and I know _ there'll be a storm to - night. _

This is get - ting se - ri - ous. Are you think-ing 'bout

you or us? Don't say _ what you're a - bout to say. _ Look back

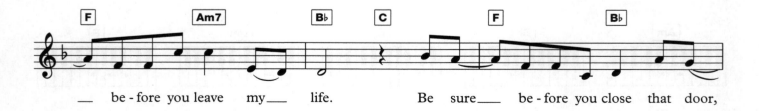

_ be - fore you leave my _ life. Be sure _ be - fore you close that door,

We Have All The Time In The World

Words by Hal David / Music by John Barry

Suggested Registration: Trumpet
Rhythm: Soft Rock
Tempo: ♩ = 96

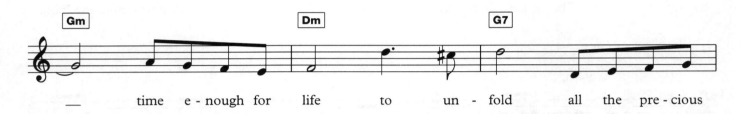

We have all the time in the world,_____

__ time e - nough for life to un - fold all the pre - cious

things love has in store. We have all the love in the

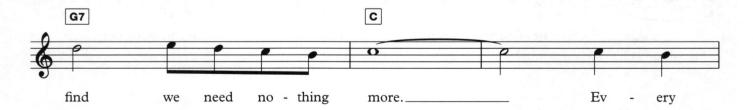

world,_____ if that's all we have, you will

find we need no - thing more._____ Ev - ery

step of the way will find us_____ with the

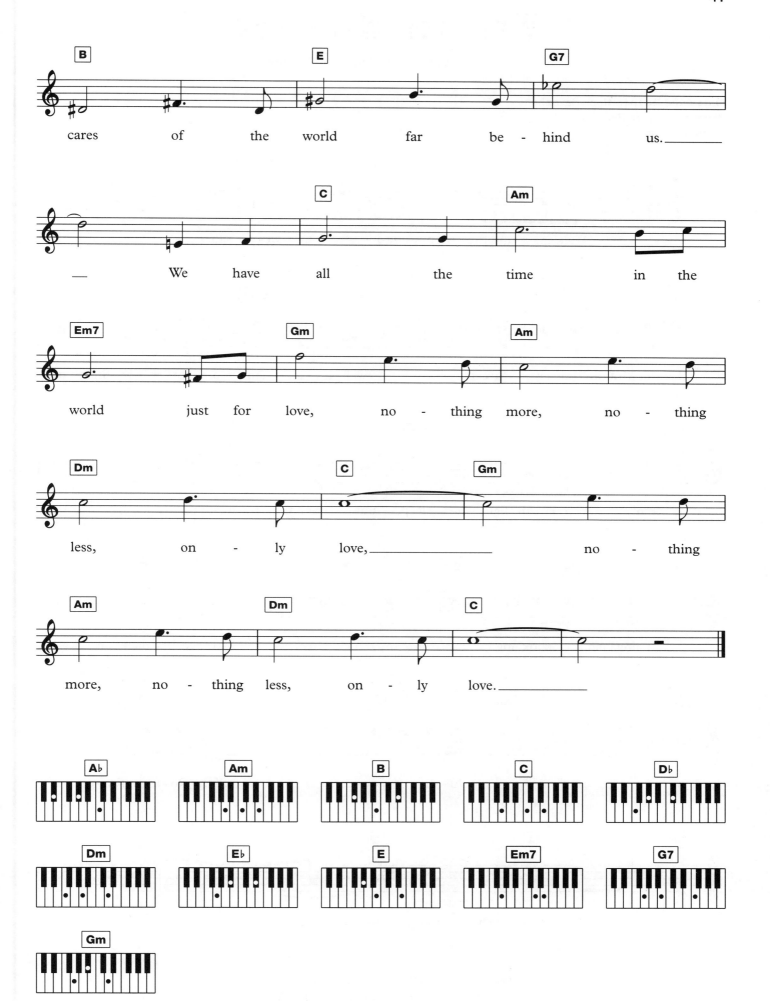

Weather With You

Words and Music by Neil Finn and Tim Finn

Suggested Registration: Saxophone
Rhythm: Slow 16 Beat
Tempo: ♩ = 96

Walk-ing round the room sing-ing stor - my wea - ther at Fif - ty

Sev - en Mount Plea-sant Street,_ well, it's the same room, but ev - ery-thing's dif -

- f'rent, you can fight the sleep, but not the dream._

Things ain't_ cook-ing in my kit-chen, strange af - flic - tion wash

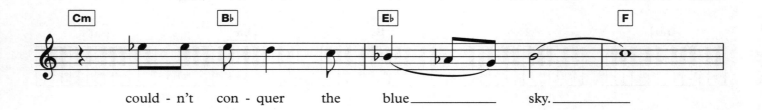

o - ver_ me. Ju - li - us Cae - sar and the Ro - man Em - pire

could - n't con - quer the blue_____ sky._____

Woman To Woman

Words and Music by Beverley Craven

Suggested Registration: Piano
Rhythm: 8 Beat
Tempo: ♩ = 98

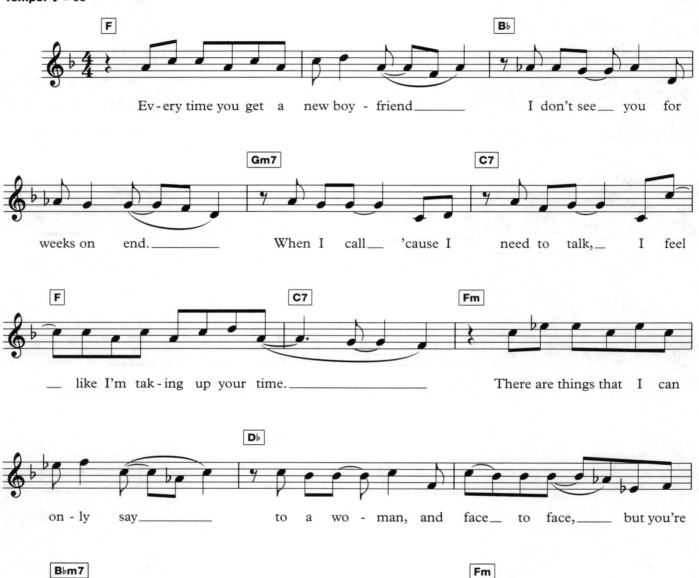

Ev-ery time you get a new boy - friend_____ I don't see__ you for weeks on end._____ When I call__ 'cause I need to talk,__ I feel __ like I'm tak-ing up your time._____ There are things that I can on - ly say_____ to a wo - man, and face__ to face,_____ but you're oc - cu - pied__ al-most ev-ery night._____ I've got a sec-ret, and I need ad - vice wo-man to wo-man. He came__ and took pos-ses - sion,__ now you ne -

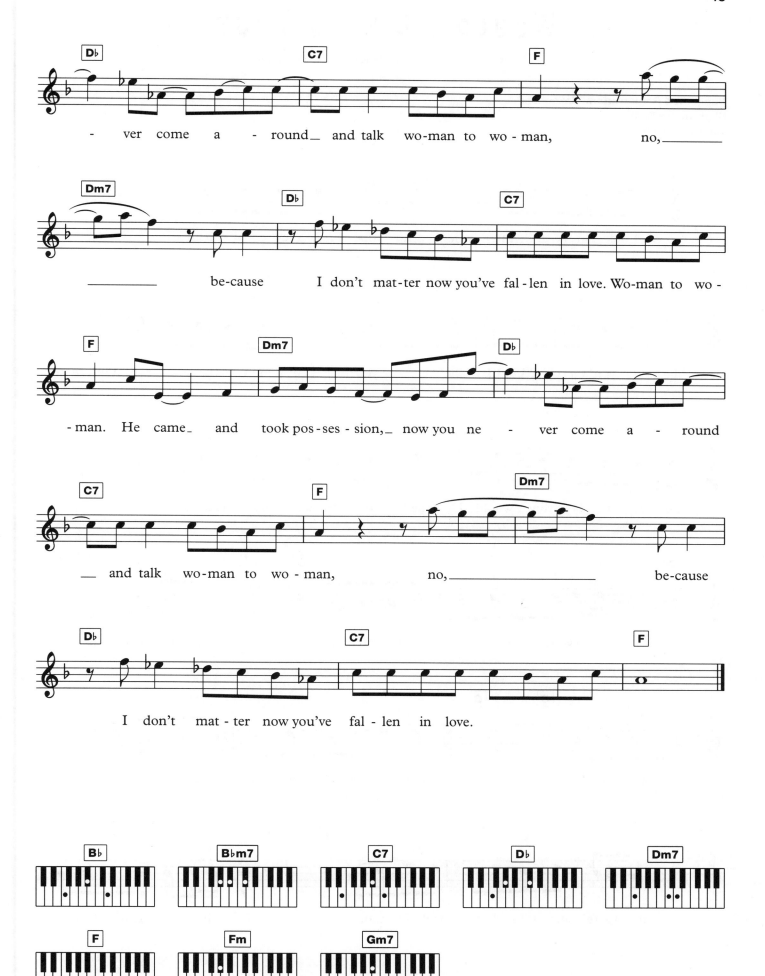

WOULD I LIE TO YOU?

Words and Music by Peter Vale and Mick Leeson

Suggested Registration: Saxophone
Rhythm: 16 Beat
Tempo: ♩ = 100

Look in-to my eyes, can't you see they're o - pen wide? Would I

lie to you ba-by? Would I lie___ to you?___ Don't you know it's true? Girl, there's

no - one else but you, would I lie to you ba - by, yeah?___

Ev-ery-bo - dy wants to know the truth, in my arms is the

on - ly proof. I hid my heart be - hind the bed-room door,___

now there's some-thin' I can't feel no more. I'm tell-in' you ba - by, you will

THE EASY KEYBOARD LIBRARY
Also available in the Decades Series

THE TWENTIES
including:

Ain't Misbehavin'
Ain't She Sweet?
Baby Face
The Man I Love

My Blue Heaven
Side By Side
Spread A Little Happiness
When You're Smiling

THE THIRTIES
including:

All Of Me
A Fine Romance
I Wanna Be Loved By You
I've Got You Under My Skin

The Lady Is A Tramp
Smoke Gets In Your Eyes
Summertime
Walkin' My Baby Back Home

THE FORTIES
including:

Almost Like Being In Love
Don't Get Around Much Any More
How High The Moon
Let There Be Love

Sentimental Journey
Swinging On A Star
Tenderly
You Make Me Feel So Young

THE FIFTIES
including:

All The Way
Cry Me A River
Dream Lover
High Hopes

Magic Moments
Mister Sandman
A Teenager In Love
Whatever Will Be Will Be

THE SIXTIES
including:

Cabaret
Happy Birthday Sweet Sixteen
I'm A Believer
The Loco-motion

My Kind Of Girl
Needles And Pins
There's A Kind Of Hush
Walk On By

THE SEVENTIES
including:

Chanson D'Amour
Hi Ho Silver Lining
I'm Not In Love
Isn't She Lovely

Save Your Kisses For Me
Take Good Care Of My Baby
We've Only Just Begun
You Light Up My Life

THE EIGHTIES
including:

Anything For You
China In Your Hand
Everytime You Go Away
Golden Brown

I Want To Break Free
Karma Chameleon
Nikita
Take My Breath Away

THE NINETIES
including:

Crocodile Shoes
I Swear
A Million Love Songs
The One And Only

Promise Me
Sacrifice
Think Twice
Would I Lie To You?